WELCOME TO
ZOOTOPIA!
A
CASE
for
Judy Hopps
© Disney

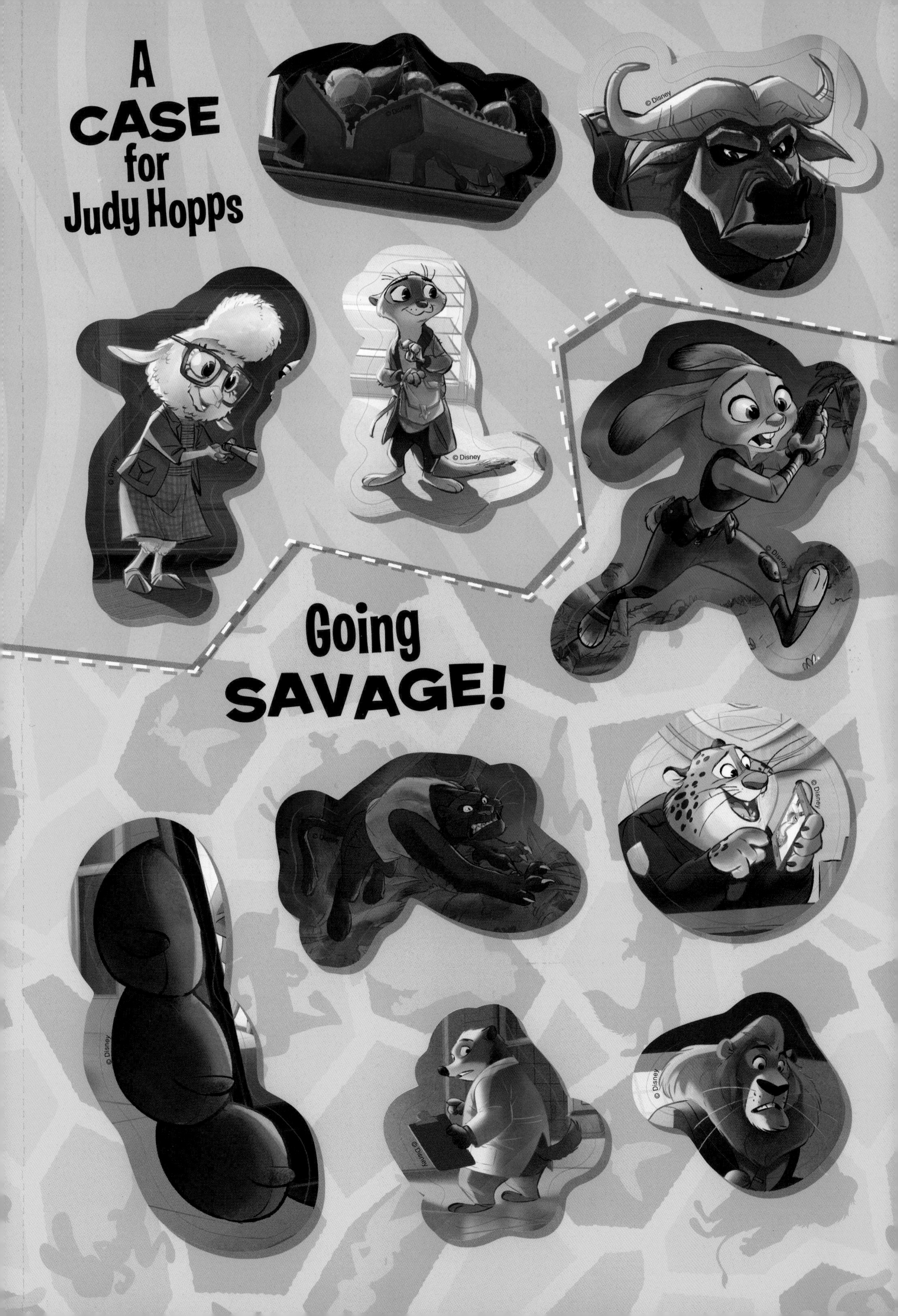
A
CASE
for
Judy Hopps
Going
SAVAGE!

PREDATORS vs. PREY
Bellwether's BUSTED!
© Disney

DISTRICT
ANYONE CAN BE ANYTHING
JUST FOR FUN
© Disney

Disney

ZOOTOPIA

STICKER SCENES

ZOOTOPIA6514

Code is valid for your ebook and may be redeemed through the Disney Story Central app on the App Store. Content subject to availability. Parent permission required. Code expires on December 31, 2019.

Bath • New York • Cologne • Melbourne • Delhi
Hong Kong • Shenzhen • Singapore • Amsterdam

WELCOME TO ZOOTOPIA!

Judy Hopps always wanted to be a police officer. Now she has left her family behind to move to the big city to do just that.

Judy will be the first rabbit ever to be a cop in the Zootopia Police Department (ZPD), and she can't wait to get started. She is a firm believer in the city's motto: "Anyone can be anything!"

But Judy's new boss, Chief Bogo, doesn't believe a rabbit can be a real cop. He puts her on parking duty instead!

On her first day, Judy overhears the manager of an ice-cream parlor refusing to serve a fox. Judy hates to see any animal treated this way. She shows her ZPD badge and orders the manager to sell the fox a Jumbo-pop for his little son.

Outside the shop, the fox says thank you and introduces himself. His name is Nick Wilde.

A CASE for Judy Hopps

Later that day, Judy sees Nick and his son again. They are melting down the Jumbo-pop to make lots of little ice "pawpsicles," then selling them! They lied to her! The little fox isn't really Nick's young son—he's Nick's partner in crime.

Judy tries to arrest Nick, but he points out that he hasn't actually done anything illegal. Then he tells Judy she'll never be a real cop. As they're arguing, she walks right into some wet cement and gets stuck! Judy can only watch as Nick walks away.

Back at the ZPD, Judy is talking with Chief Bogo when an otter storms in. She's upset about her husband, Emmitt, who has been missing for ten days. Judy sees this as her chance to prove herself and offers to find Emmitt.

Before Chief Bogo can refuse Judy's offer, Assistant Mayor Bellwether arrives. She is so pleased that a rabbit is being given a big chance as a police officer, Chief Bogo can't argue. But he gives Judy just two days to solve the case. If she fails, she has to leave the ZPD.

Going SAVAGE!

In Emmitt's case file, Judy sees a photograph of the missing otter holding one of Nick's pawpsicles! She finds Nick and convinces him to help her.

They find the last animal to see Emmitt—a jaguar called Manchas. He tells them the otter went crazy, yelling something about "night howlers," and ran off. Then suddenly, Manchas hunches over on to all fours and starts chasing after Judy and Nick!

Eventually, Judy manages to trap the jaguar and call for police backup. But by the time Chief Bogo arrives, Manchas has disappeared!

Nick and Judy discover that a pack of wolves kidnapped Manchas. They must be the night howlers!

The wolves had taken Manchas to a huge abandoned building. Nick and Judy race there and sneak inside. They find fifteen animals, including Manchas and Emmitt, all locked in cages and acting savagely.

Suddenly, somebody arrives and Nick and Judy hide. As they watch, Lionheart, the mayor of Zootopia, walks in. He's the one who has locked up these animals! Judy records him on her phone as he talks to a doctor.

"Something has awakened their savage instincts," the doctor explains.

PREDATORS vs. PREY

Back at the ZPD, Judy plays her phone recording to Chief Bogo. He praises her work and has Mayor Lionheart arrested for locking up the animals. Assistant Mayor Bellwether will now be Mayor of Zootopia!

Later, Judy speaks to the press and tells them that only predator animals are turning savage, not prey species.

As a predator himself, Nick is upset. He storms off, knowing that Judy's words will cause a lot of trouble between the prey and predator animals in the city.

Judy is sad to see the city so divided, and she can't help but feel like she is to blame.

"I wanted to make the world better. But I made it worse," she says sadly. She decides to quit the ZPD.

Soon after, back at her family farm, Judy overhears her father mention "night howlers." Judy realizes they are flowers, not wolves at all! Something in these flowers has a strange effect on animals, making them go wild.

Judy races back to the city. She finds Nick and apologizes. She tells him they have to find out who's using the night howlers on the predators!

Bellwether's BUSTED!

Judy and Nick get on the trail of the night howlers until they finally find an old subway car full of them! They watch as a sheep loads a dart gun with the flowers' pollen.

Right then, Judy and Nick realize this is all Bellwether's plan! She wants to make the animals in the city scared of one another, so she can have power over everyone.

Judy and Nick manage to grab the dart gun—now they have their evidence. They steal the subway car and head back toward the ZPD, taking a shortcut through an empty museum.

Bellwether is at the museum! She grabs the dart gun from Nick and Judy, then pushes them into a pit in the floor of the museum. They are trapped. Bellwether takes the dart gun out of the case and fires a pellet at Nick!

Nick turns savage and snarls at Judy, but then he stops suddenly. Bellwether is confused. Nick smiles. He replaced the night-howler pellet in the case with a harmless blueberry! He has also recorded everything that's happened with a secret microphone. Just then, the ZPD arrives and arrests Bellwether.

ANYONE CAN BE ANYTHING

Once Bellwether is gone and the savage animals are cured, Zootopia returns to normal—and Nick joins the ZPD!

"Still believe it?" Nick asks Judy as they sit in their patrol car.

"That anyone can be anything?" Judy says. "Mmm, yeah, I do. Even if it's not quite as simple as all that."

Suddenly, a red sports car speeds past them. Nick turns on the siren and Judy hits the accelerator. It's time to fight some crime!